# Zolemina

## The Should Do Could Do Would Do Cat

Written by Ania Danylo

Illustrated by David Griffiths

Illustrations by David Griffiths
Book Design and Layout by Ania Danylo
ISBN 978-1-9991441-7-3

For Zoey, my fabulous feline friend who would rather listen to music...than catch a mouse.

Zolemina, she stood

At the end of her block.

She stood very still

Staring hard at the rock.

It wouldn't be long

'Fore she wanted to move.

She wanted to dance.

She wanted to groove.

"But cats, they don't dance..."

Was the phrase she had heard,

Her self-esteem slipped.

Now her dream seemed absurd.

Her job was to hunt,

Yes, for fish, birds and mice.

Still, deep in her heart,

Hunting didn't feel nice.

An artist she was
In her heart and her soul.

Her passion she'd find
'Fore she got too darned old.

Well, painting it seemed

Might be just right for her.

She tried with her tail,

But the paint burnt her fur.

Then soon she began

To start telling some jokes.

She tried very hard,

But the laughter was broke.

"So singing," she mused,

"Might be something for me."

She opened her mouth,

But got stung by a bee.

"Where's something out there
That is just right for me?"
Her spirit grew weak,
As she dropped to one knee.

A bird came along
And asked why she was down?
"I'm an artist," she cried,
"But I can't find my ground."

"I saw you last night,"

Said the bird with a tweet,

"Jumping and spinning,

You were swaying so sweet."

The cat blurted out,

"Dancing cats are called nerds.

I've always been told,

You should leave it for birds."

"Why would you listen?
And what fool told you so?
It's your life to live.
You should follow your soul.

The cat gave a pause,

But soon started to sway.

First left, then to right,

Then she danced all the day.

Next morning she woke,

So surprised, what she saw!

A gift by her side.

It was right by her paw.

A new dress was there.

It was purple and pink.

Both colours she loved,

Making both her eyes blink!

"This must be a sign

Of just what I should do.

If dance is my thing,

I must look for some shoes."

She turned and she saw,

Very much to her glee,

Ballet shoes to match!

Tucked in right by the tree.

Who gave such nice gifts?

It seemed rather absurd.

She looked all around,

And then soon saw the bird.

Flying around her,

Far above the grand tree,

Chirping out loudly,

"They're from me, they're from me!"

"Gosh, thanks," said the cat

To the bird in the sky.

The bird couldn't hear,

He was flying too high.

ne leapt with her strength

a branch of the tree.

re they really from you?

re they really for me?"

The bird had flown down.

He was close to the cat.

"From me, just for you!"

On the same branch they sa

The cat was quite stunned

By the kindness he showed.

The gifts seemed so much,

That her kitty face glowed.

"I saw you were sad,

With your face on the ground.

I had to do something,

So the answer I found".

The cat gave a shrug,

Then she tried on the dress.

The shoes she laced up.

They were both a success!

The bird he did smile,

As he stretched out a wing.

The cat now was dancing,

First a fox-trot, then swing.

"This is your passion,
And an artist you are!
I must fly home now
To play my guitar."

The cat she was brimming,

Not feeling forlorn.

Her dancing grew strong

With her spirit reborn.

She practiced a year,

Through the rain, sleet and snow.

Her burning desire

Was to put on a show.

The rock that had blocked

All her instincts to move,

Is where she'd perform!

Soon by it, she would groove!

With all of her strength

he'd collect many rocks,

o build her own stage,

Vith a mouse and a fox.

She was bold and ablaze
As the audience grew.
Her dreams now fulfilled,
To herself, she was true.

This cat ballet show,

So far from the norm;

Crowds cheered very loud

As they watched her perform!

Who cheered the loudest?

T'was the bird in the sky.

Proudly he watched her,

As a tear filled his eye.

ney came from afar,

r a chance, just to glance!

ow all the world knew,

olemina...would...dance!

## About The Author

Ania Danylo has been an actor, writer, director, teacher, and acting coach for more than 25 years. She has written and produced numerous children's plays. Ania enjoys all her teaching and coaching sessions with her wonderful students. She is specially fond of the storytelling classes!

"Zolemina The Should Do Could Do Would Do Cat," is Ania's second published children's book. She published her first book "The Elephant's Christmas Wish" in 2019, and a colouring book version of it was published in 2022.

You can reach Ania through her website at aniadanylo.com

Printed in the USA
CPSIA information can be obtained
at www.ICGtesting.com
LVHW070808181023
761236LV00071B/1395